1. The nuclear-propelled missile submarine is the most survivable of the existing strategic weapon systems. The United States began an intensive effort to develop a ballistic missile submarine (SSBN) in the mid-1950s to counter the Soviet development of land-based ballistic missiles and, later, the technology potential indicated by the orbiting of the Sputnik satellite in October 1957. The initial US submarine effort was the Polaris programme, with 41 nuclear-propelled submarines completed between 1960 and 1967. *Ohio* (SSBN-728) was the first of the next, Trident-series submarines, completed from 1981 onwards. (US Navy Official)

WARSHIPS ILLUSTRATED No 2

The US NAVY Today

Volume I NORMAN POLMAR

ARMS AND ARMOUR PRESS

Introduction

Published in 1985 by Arms and Armour Press,
2–6 Hampstead High Street, London NW3 1QQ.

Distributed in the United States by
Sterling Publishing Co. Inc., 2 Park Avenue,
New York, N.Y. 10016.

British Library Cataloguing in Publication Data:
Polmar, Norman
The U.S. navy today. – (Warships illustrated; no. 2)
Vol. I
1. Warship – United States
I. Title   II. Series
623.8′25′0973   VA58.4
ISBN 0-85368-718-8

Editing, design and artwork by Roger Chesneau.
Typesetting by Typesetters (Birmingham) Ltd.
Printed in Italy by Tipolitografia G. Canale
& C. S.p.A., Turin, in association with Keats
European Ltd.

◀2
2. The *Nimitz* (CVN-68) Class aircraft carriers are the
largest warships ever built: the lead-ship, shown here,
displaces almost 94,000 tons fully loaded and has a
length of 1,092ft. This overhead view shows the flight
deck arrangement as the carrier takes on stores from an
ammunition ship steaming alongside. One of the three
starboard deck-edge lifts that connect the flight and
hangar decks can be seen in the lowered position; there
is a fourth lift on the after port side. The angled deck
landing area is clearly marked, and there are four steel
arresting cables at the after end. (US Navy Official)

The Reagan Administration came into office in January 1981 riding on
the crest of American public support for an increase in military posture.
The Soviet invasion of Afghanistan, the holding of the American
embassy staff by Iran's Revolutionary government and Soviet advances
in strategic and conventional weapons had been effectively translated
by the politicians into a call for improved US military capabilities.
During the 1970s the US Navy had declined from a peak Vietnam
strength of almost 1,000 ships in active commission to only 445 such
vessels at the time President Reagan was elected – the smallest number
of ships in the active fleet since before the Second World War.

The man selected by Reagan to head the naval build-up was 39-year-
old John Lehman. He became Secretary of the Navy with probably a
better understanding of the USN than any secretary since James
Forrestal, who had served in this capacity from 1944 to 1947 (when he
became the first US Secretary of Defense). Lehman put forward an
aggressive Navy programme, generally publicized as goal of 600 ships.

More important than numbers was Lehman's proposed composition
of that fleet: fifteen aircraft carrier battle groups, four surface action
groups centred on battleships, sufficient amphibious ships to lift a
Marine division and a separate brigade, and at least 100 nuclear attack
submarines, plus the myriad support ships. Not addressed in these
goals was the Navy's strategic submarine force – the Poseidon and
Trident missile submarines and their support ships. The Navy in early
1985 has 31 older nuclear submarines each armed with sixteen
Poseidon or Trident missiles, plus five modern *Ohio* Class submarines
each carrying 24 Trident missiles.

The US Navy is a balanced force, capable of a variety of forward
operations in peacetime, periods of crisis, and conventional conflict. A
large force of cruisers and destroyers provides anti-air and anti-
submarine defence of carrier battle groups, whilst some destroyers as
well as smaller frigates provide escort of military and merchant
convoys, amphibious groups, and replenishment ships. There is a
Marine Corps of three large combat divisions and three air wings, and
the Navy operates sixty large amphibious ships, including twelve
helicopter carriers that have a total lift capacity of about one reinforced
Marine division. Mine warfare is a traditionally weak aspect of the US
Navy but two new classes of surface minesweeping ships intended to
clear American ports and coastal waters of mines laid by foreign
submarines are currently under construction; one class (designated
MCM) has a conventional configuration while the smaller MSH type
will be based on an air-cushion vehicle design.

The only 'small combatants' operated by the US Navy are six
hydrofoil missile-patrol craft (the survivors of an ambitious programme of the early 1970s), but there is a considerable force of riverine
craft manned by reserve units, an effort to retain the extensive body of
knowledge in riverine/coastal combat built up in the Vietnam War. A
large number of auxiliary ships are in service, and there are also a few
miscellaneous auxiliaries – cable ships, a missile test ship and a training
carrier. Finally, the Navy has several hundred small service craft that
operate at US and foreign naval bases.

In addition to the aircraft embarked on aircraft carriers, the Navy has
a large land-based air arm, consisting of anti-submarine/maritime
patrol aircraft, reconnaissance aircraft, transports and training aircraft,
as well as a large air research and development organization. To these
may be added the three Marine combat air wings. The Navy provides
basic air training for the Marine Corps (as well as for the US Coast
Guard, which has a small air arm).

For the foreseeable future the Navy will remain a major force in
supporting US political, economic and military goals in a world that
continues to be highly dependent upon the use of the seas in peace and
in war.

Norman Polmar

▲3

▲4

3. The *Ohio* Class Trident submarines are the largest undersea craft yet built in the West, with a submerged displacement of 18,700 tons and an overall length of 560ft; only the Soviet *Typhoon* Class missile submarines are larger, displacing some 25,000 tons. Being built at a rate of one boat annually, the *Ohio*s each have 24 missile tubes. The small amount of structure visible when the submarine is on the surface belies the vessel's true size. (US Navy Official)

4. Like a fish out of water, *Ohio* lies immobile in dry dock at the Trident base at Bangor, Washington. Note the stern control surfaces; the tapered stern is capped by a single propeller. The submarine's size – her circular hull has a maximum diameter of 42ft – was dictated primarily by the diameter of her nuclear propulsion plant. Her defensive armament consists of four torpedo tubes fitted just forward of the sail (fin) structure, two each to port and starboard. (US Navy Official)

5. The Trident submarine *Michigan* (SSBN-727) under construction at the General Dynamics/Electric Boat yard at Groton, Connecticut;

there is a construction ring around her bow and some of her missile tube hatches are open. Electric Boat and the Newport News shipyard in Virginia are the only US yards now building nuclear submarines, although in the 1960s, at the height of the Polaris programme, seven American yards were engaged in their construction. *Michigan* took six years from keel-laying to completion. (US Navy Official)

6. A Trident C-4 practice missile streaks skyward from *John C. Calhoun* (SSBN-630). When firing a missile the submarine is completely submerged, and inertial navigation devices within the boat provide an exact location independent of external 'fixes', permitting the missile to be fired with a high degree of accuracy. The C-4 carries eight nuclear re-entry vehicles ('bombs') that can be aimed at separate targets and has a range of some 4,000 nautical miles. The earlier Poseidon was the world's first operational missile carrying Multiple Independently targeted Re-entry Vehicles (MIRV). (US Navy Official)

▼5

6▶

▲7   ▼8

7. *Henry L. Stimson* (SSBN-655) is one of 41 Polaris missile submarines completed from 1960 to 1967; all were originally built to carry the Polaris missile, but 31 of the *Lafayette* (SSBN-616) Class were subsequently modified to fire the multi-warhead Poseidon. During the early 1980s the last twelve submarines were again updated and now have the Trident C-4. The Trident D-5 now under development, to be carried by the *Ohio* Class, will have a range of about 6,000 miles. (General Dynamics/Electric Boat)

8. A rare sight: a strategic missile submarine at high speed. *Sam Rayburn* (SSBN-635) and other submarines of this type spend most of their time at sea submerged, at slow speed and in a state of electronic silence. They transmit radio messages only in dire emergency, but regularly come near the surface to trail a wire antenna to receive the steady stream of communications that are sent to US submarines at sea. (US Navy Official)

9. The low-lying configuration of a nuclear submarine is shown in this view of *Will Rogers* (SSBN-659) arriving alongside a support ship at Holy Loch, Scotland, with the aid of a Navy harbour tug. The bits, cleats and winches on the hull are retracted when the submarine is at sea, providing a smooth hull to minimize the noise of water flowing over it. At sea men venture on to the hull only with safety lines attached to tracks that run along the entire deck. (US Navy Official)

10. *Stonewall Jackson* (SSBN-634) loads a missile at Bangor, Washington. Submarine ballistic missiles are transported and stored in these containers; they are positioned over the submarine's missile tubes and the missiles lowered through them. The ten oldest Polaris submarines have been retired or modified for temporary use as attack submarines (SSN); of the 31 submarines refitted to carry Poseidon, nineteen will be retired in the next few years, the other twelve having been modified to carry the Trident C-4. (US Navy Official)

9▲   10▼

11. *Sam Rayburn* with missile tubes open; 'billard game' markings can be seen on the insides of the outer hatches. Although the Soviet Navy developed submarine-launched ballistic missiles before the United States, the high priority given to the Polaris programme provided a major technological breakthrough in strategic weapons development in a remarkably short time. Early plans to carry Polaris missiles in surface ships, including multinational manned NATO ships, were discarded. (Newport News Shipbuilding)

12. After a two-month missile patrol in northern waters, *Sam Rayburn* comes alongside a submarine tender at Holy Loch; the tender can remove and replace or check missiles and torpedoes. An alternative crew has been flown out from the United States, and during a brief refit period the crews will change over and the submarine will be provisioned and receive any necessary repairs. Missile submarine bases are also located at New London, Connecticut; Kings Bay, Georgia; and Bangor, Washington. (US Navy Official)

13. US submarine-deployed ballistic missiles are launched underwater, but this unusual view shows *Henry Clay* (SSBN-625) firing a Polaris A-2 missile from the surface; note the debris from the fibreglass protective covering, the single open missile hatch and the special telemetry mast attached to the submarine for the purposes of the test. The only full test of the US strategic weapon system occurred on 6 May 1962, when the submarine *Ethan Allen* (SSBN-608) fired a nuclear-tipped Polaris in the Pacific. (US Navy Official)

◄11

12▲   13▼

14. A modern nuclear-propelled attack submarine at high speed on the surface: this is *San Francisco* (SSN-711), one of the large *Los Angeles* (SSN-688) Class, of which more than forty have been laid down since 1976. These submarines have a submerged displacement of 6,900 tons – more than the Polaris submarines – and a length of 360ft. Their size is dictated principally by the large nuclear powerplant and the sound isolation of machinery and other noise-reducing features. (Newport News Shipbuilding)

15. The *Los Angeles* Class submarine *Omaha* (SSN-692) prepares to moor. One of the periscopes is at full elevation, and the small navigation radar is visible atop the sail structure, just forward of the periscope. The sail provides a small navigation bridge, but its main purpose is to house the submarine's periscopes and masts and to hold the diving planes that, with the stern planes, control depth when the boat is submerged. There is a sonar dome forward. (Giorgio Arra)

▲14   ▼15

16. *Hawkbill* (SSN-637) is one of 37 *Sturgeon* (SSN-637) Class attack submarines completed from 1967 to 1975. These are similar to the *Los Angeles* Class except that a larger propulsion plant makes them about 5kts faster underwater, giving a top speed in excess of 30kts (the hull shape of modern submarines makes them faster submerged than on the surface). SSNs are designed primarily for hunting and destroying enemy submarines. (Giorgio Arra)

17. A Mk. 48 long-range torpedo is loaded into an SSN; the 'fish' will be lowered two decks, to the amidships torpedo room. A modern SSN carries about two dozen tube-launched weapons, comprising Mk. 48 torpedoes, SUBROC rocket-delivered nuclear depth bombs, cruise missiles or mines. The Mk. 48, with a range of about 25nm, has acoustic homing guidance and can receive additional instructions from the submarine after launch by means of a thin guidance wire. (US Air Force)

16▲ 17▼

▲18

▼19

18. Modern US attack submarines have their bows given over to sonar, placing the acoustic detection equipment as far as possible from machinery and propeller noise. This sphere would be installed in the bow of an SSN after being fitted with hydrophones for detecting an enemy submarine's noises. At top and bottom are steel supports that fit it to the submarine, and on the right is an access hatch that will lead into the SSN's inner (pressure) hull. The sonar installation means that the torpedo tubes have to be fitted amidships, angled out to each side. (US Navy Official)

19. In the late 1970s, after some fifteen years of relying on carrier-based aircraft for naval strike, the US Navy began deploying the Harpoon anti-ship missile. This 60-mile weapon can be launched by aircraft or surface ships or, as shown here, from a submarine's torpedo tube. The missile is carried in and fired from a canister which falls away during launch, the control surfaces of the weapon deploying after exit. (McDonnell Douglas)

20. The Tomahawk cruise missile has followed the Harpoon into service. This is a larger weapon, available as an Anti-Ship Missile (T-ASM) with a range of several hundred miles or a Land-Attack Missile (T-LAM) carrying a conventional or nuclear warhead to a target more than a thousand miles away; *Los Angeles* Class SSNs are being provided with twelve vertical-launch Tomahawk tubes. This test missile has a nose instrument probe. (General Dynamics)

21. The *Sturgeon* Class submarine *Batfish* (SSN-681) shows her clean lines, narrow sail structure and sail-mounted diving planes. When on patrol the hull numbers are painted out. The dark 'window' on the sail and the small projections on the after deck are for the ship's sonars. Housed in the sail are periscopes, radar and radio antennae, the electronic intercept mast and the snorkel air intake for the craft's emergency diesel-electric propulsion. (General Dynamics/Electric Boat)

22. A photograph of *Sea Devil* (SSN-664) being launched, showing the submarine's circular hull design; her crew provides an indication of scale. Modern SSNs each have crews of about twelve officers and 115 enlisted men, more than half of whom have undergone lengthy nuclear power training; only nuclear trained officers can rise to command nuclear submarines. (Newport News Shipbuilding)

23. *Whale* (SSN-638) seen surfaced at the North Pole, with members of her crew out on the ice. *Sturgeon* Class SSNs are specially configured for Arctic operations: their sail-mounted diving planes rotate to a vertical position, they have a strenthened sail structure, and special sonars are fitted for under-ice navigation. The later *Los Angeles* Class lack these features, a matter of considerable importance in view of the long Arctic coast of the Soviet Union and the Soviet Navy's northern operating areas. (US Navy Official)

22▶

▼23

24▲

◄25

24. *Skate* (SSN-578) is typical of the older US nuclear attack submarines. Completed in the late 1950s, she has a conventional submarine hull form, providing a higher speed on the surface than underwater for a given horsepower. These boats, which also lack advanced sonar and SUBROC capabilities, are now suitable only for training and are being retired. (Giorgio Arra)

25. The three *Barbel* (SS-580) Class submarines were the last non-nuclear combat submarines built by the US Navy, being completed in 1959, and they will remain in active service until the late 1980s. Recent support by members of Congress, naval experts and younger naval officers for the construction of a small number of modern diesel submarines for the US Navy has been steadfastly opposed by the Navy's leadership despite the diesel boats' low cost, low crew requirements and general usefulness in several important roles. (US Navy Official)

17

▲26

26. The diesel-electric *Grayback* (SS-574) was built as a cruise missile submarine for the surface-launched Regulus land-attack missile. After that weapon was phased out she was 'mothballed' until her conversion to a transport submarine to carry some seventy commandos or 'frogmen', her two former missile hangars (one is shown here with the hatch open) being used for small boats and swimmer delivery vehicles. *Grayback* is rated as an attack submarine and does possess torpedo tubes, but her hull form makes her slow and noisy. (Giorgio Arra)

27. *Dolphin* (AGSS-555) is a special research submarine designed for very deep operation; completed in 1968, the 930-ton, 152ft craft was the last non-nuclear submarine built for the US Navy. The single torpedo tube originally mounted has been removed, but *Dolphin* has been fitted with various sonars and has been used in aircraft-to-submarine laser communication experiments. (US Navy Official)

28. A view of the nuclear-powered carrier *Nimitz*. Two large reactor plants can drive the ship at more than 30kts with a range, between nuclear core refuellings, of almost one million miles, or 13 years at cruising speeds. *Nimitz* and two sister-ships are in service; three similar ships now under construction will be completed 1987–92. (US Navy Official)

29. A crowded area of a carrier's flight deck: visible are A-7E Corsair attack planes and EA-6B Prowler electronic warfare aircraft. The larger US carriers operate some 85–90 aircraft, all as capable as their land-based counterparts and some, for example the F-14 Tomcat, F-4 Phantom, A-6 Intruder, A-4 Skyhawk and A-1 Skyraider, setting the standards for their type and generation. Note the folded wings on these aircraft to facilitate their handling and stowage aboard ship. (US Navy Official)

▼27

28▲ 29▼

19

30. The island structure of a modern aircraft carrier (that of *Dwight D. Eisenhower*, CVN-69, is shown) provides bridge and aircraft control stations and supports various radar, radio and other electronic antennae. Carrier islands are on the starboard side of the flight deck, probably because early British carrier aircraft had engine torque that pulled them to the left; some Japanese carriers did have a port-side island. (Giorgio Arra)

31. The No. 1 recessed catapult track of the carrier *Nimitz*. Each of the four 'cats', some 300ft long, can launch a fully loaded aircraft into

▲31

the air every minute. The US Navy's steam catapults, angled flight deck and mirror landing system, as well as the basic concept of the aircraft carrier, can be traced to British naval developments. (US Navy Official)

32. The hangar deck of a *Nimitz* provides space to maintain and store about half of a Carrier Air Wing. The bright white lighting shown here can be changed to red for night operations in forward areas. (US Navy Official)

▼32

33. An F-14A Tomcat fighter leaves a carrier. The aircraft's wings change incidence automatically, extending for landing, take-off and cruise flight and sweeping back for high-speed flight and manoeuvring. The Tomcat's radar can detect aircraft more than 100 miles away and the primary Phoenix missiles, of which up to six can be carried, can be fired against aircraft more than 60 miles away. The Tomcat also carries Sidewinder and Sparrow missiles, and a rotary-barrel 20mm Gatling-type gun. (US Navy Official)

34. With undercarriage and arresting hook lowered, an F-14A Tomcat streaks across the deck of a carrier; a moment later the hook will engage one of the four arresting cables and the aircraft will be pulled to a halt with a short run-out. Note the two-seat cockpit, the rear station being occupied by a radar intercept officer. Some F-14s can be fitted with a camera and infra-red reconnaissance pod (TARPS) for recce flights. (US Navy Official)

▲35 ▼36

37▲

35. The well-known F-4 Phantom is still to be seen aboard several carriers in the fighter role (and is flown from shore bases by the Marine Corps). Here mechanics prepare for flight an F-4 laden with Sidewinder missiles and an auxiliary fuel tank. A carrier can provide a full range of maintenance for its aircraft, and stores, fuel and weapons for several days of combat operations; however, even the nuclear carriers must take on provisions, aviation fuel and weapons every few days. (US Navy Official)

36. An A-7 Corsair attack plane is raised from the hangar deck to the flight deck of a carrier on one of four deck-edge lifts. (US Navy Official)

37. The F/A-18 Hornet is being procured by the Navy to replace the F-4 Phantom and A-7 Corsair, and by the Marine Corps to replace the Phantom. The single-seat Hornet can be employed in either the fighter or attack role, needing only minor changes to its weapon

racks. However, its procurement has been controversial, and far fewer are expected to enter service than the 1,366 originally planned for Navy and Marine use starting in 1983. The smaller USMC order is partially due to the Marines' decision to buy the AV-8B Harrier II instead of the F/A-18 for the attack role. (US Navy Official)

38. Here seen being prepared for a catapult 'shot', the A-6 Intruder is the Navy/Marine medium attack plane, with a long range, a heavy weapons payload and an elaborate all-weather/night strike capability. Note the large nose radome and the refuelling probe projecting in front of the two-man cockpit. Carrier aircraft markings include letters identifying the wing (in this case 'AG'), the squadron (the '500' series is the medium attack squadron) and aircraft in squadron ('506' on nose and '06' on tail). The aircraft's serial number (151583) and ship name (*Independence*) are also visible. In combat, low-visibility markings would be used. (US Navy Official)

38▼

39. Despite modern technology, navies still require muscle and sweat, especially aboard aircraft carriers. Here a sailor pushes a cart of 500lb bombs towards a waiting aircraft on the carrier *Constellation* (CV-64). These are Snakeye bombs, with fins that extend when the weapons are released to retard their fall and permit an aircraft to escape safely in very low-level attacks; fuses will be inserted in the bombs' nose cavities. 'Iron' bombs still have a role in combat as well as guided bombs and missiles, as demonstrated in the 1982 Anglo-Argentine war over the Falklands. (US Navy Official)

40. The EA-6B Prowler – one is shown here about to touch down on the carrier *Ranger* (CV-61) – is the electronic jamming version of the A-6, its radar/radio detection and jammer equipment being carried in pods. Note the smaller nose radome, the enlarged cockpit for the crew of four, and the electronics pod on the tail fin. Four of the EA-6B models are provided in each Air Wing and the aircraft are also flown from ashore (and on occasion from carriers) by the Marine Corps. (US Navy Official)

41. Attack submarines are assuming new importance for the US Navy: since the Second World War they have been used primarily for anti-submarine operations, with a secondary anti-shipping role, but now there is increasing interest in the use of SSNs for escorting carrier battle groups and for long-range strike with Tomahawk cruise missiles. (US Navy Official)

42. A *Los Angeles* Class submarine demonstrates an emergency surfacing evolution during her sea trials. Water pours from the sail structure and the sail-mounted diving planes, and note the submarine's relatively pointed bow, which houses a large sonar dome. Her torpedo tubes are amidships, angled out, two to each side. (US Navy Official)

▲39   ▼40

▲44

43. (Previous spread) The modern US aircraft carrier is the largest warship afloat, yet it is still a small speck on the ocean's surface. The Soviet Union has developed an extensive, world-wide ocean surveillance system to keep track of US aircraft carriers, which they still consider a threat to the Soviet homeland. About half of a carrier's Air Wing can be stowed in the hangar, the rest normally being parked on the flight deck while still leaving room for air operations. (US Navy Official)

44. The aircraft carrier *Ranger* (CV-61) about to go to sea; note the aircraft parked on her forward flight deck. US aircraft carriers normally spend seven months deployed to forward areas – the

Western Pacific, Indian or Atlantic Oceans – followed by a year in their home ports, in overhaul and engaged in local training and other operations. (Lt. Peter Clayton)

45. The E-2 Hawkeye airborne early warning (AEW) aircraft gives the appearance of an aeroplane captured by a flying saucer. The rotating circular radome atop the aircraft can detect air and surface targets out to distances of about 200nm and direct fighters or attack aircraft to these targets. Use of the E-2 also allows a task force to remain 'electronically silent', with its radars turned off and the AEW aircraft providing radar surveillance and communications for the force. (US Navy Official)

▼45

46. All carrier-based fighter and attack aircraft can be refuelled in flight by carrier-based KA-6D Intruders, which are specially configured for that role, or from 'buddy stores' carried on other fighter and attack aircraft. This is the co-pilot's view from an A-6 Intruder being refuelled by a KA-6D. (US Navy Official)
47. A bomb-laden A-7 Corsair is prepared for launch from an aircraft carrier. The A-7 is a light attack aircraft, capable of carrying a variety of air-to-surface weapons for delivery against surface ships or ground targets; a pair of self-defence Sidewinder missiles can also be carried, as shown. The F/A-18 Hornet is scheduled to replace the A-7 in Carrier Wings, providing 24 aircraft that could be used in the fighter as well as the light attack role. (US Navy Official)

48. The threat to surface ships from hostile submarines is increasing, and most US aircraft carriers each have a squadron of S-3A Viking fixed-wing aircraft and SH-3H Sea King helicopters for anti-submarine warfare (ASW). The Viking's sonobuoy dispensers and tail hook are visible in the rear of the fuselage in this view. The aircraft have internal weapons bays and wing pylons for ASW torpedoes, rockets and mines, and they can detect submarines with sonobuoys, radar, and infra-red and magnetic detectors. (Robert Lawson)

49. An SH-3 Sea King from the carrier *Independence* (CV-62) lowers its 'dipping' sonar into the water. These ASW helicopters carry ASW torpedoes and can also operate from the large *Spruance* (DD-963) Class destroyers; the slightly smaller SH-60B Seahawk/LAMPS helicopter has been developed for use aboard destroyers and frigates. (US Navy Official)

50. In addition to the three *Nimitz* Class nuclear-propelled carriers, the Navy has one older nuclear 'flat-top', *Enterprise* (CVN-65); eight ships of the general *Forrestal* (CV-59) design; and two older ships of the *Midway* (CV-41) Class. This is *Forrestal*, the first of the 'super carriers', completed in 1955; the ship is shown refuelling from the British oiler *Olna*. These carriers have an nominal 30-year service life, which is being extended to 45–50 years through a modernization called SLEP (Service Life Extension Program). (US Navy Official)

◄48

49▲ 50▼

▲51   ▼52

53▲

51. *Midway* was one of three large or 'battle' carriers (CVB) completed in 1945–47, the largest American ships of the Second World War period. Two of them, *Midway* (home-ported in Japan) and *Coral Sea*, continue in active service and are not expected to be retired until about 1990. Although they cannot operate F-14 fighters or S-3A ASW aircraft, they do carry other first-line aircraft, demonstrating the longevity and flexibility of the design. (Giorgio Arra)

52. The four *Iowa* (BB-61) Class battleships are the only ships of this type remaining with any navy. This is *New Jersey* (BB-62), which saw service in the Second World War and in the Vietnamese conflicts and was again taken out of 'mothballs' and recommissioned in 1982. Displacing 57,500 tons fully loaded and 887ft long, she carries nine 16in guns and is fitted with Harpoon and Tomahawk missiles. At least one more ship, *Iowa* herself, will be recommissioned during the current US fleet build-up. (US Navy Official)

53. The battleship *New Jersey*, shown here at anchor in 1983, reveals the long, clean lines of the *Iowa* Class dreadnoughts, which are the largest battleships ever built except for the short-lived Japanese *Yamato* and *Musashi*, both sunk by US carrier bombers late in the Second World War. During the war the *Iowa*s served mainly in the anti-aircraft role, defending fast carrier groups, but in Korea all four ships, and in Vietnam *New Jersey*, were used for shore bombardment. (Giorgio Arra)

54. Crewmen on board *New Jersey* move a powder case for a 16in gun during ordnance loading. Several such powder bags are used to fire armour-piercing shells each weighing 2,700lb out to a range of 40,200yds. However, the absence of foreign armoured ships, except for a couple of Soviet units, means that the reactivated *Iowa*s will have mostly shore-bombardment shells, weighing 1,900lb and firing to a range of 41,600yds. Each of the nine 16in guns can fire at a maximum rate of two rounds per minute. (US Navy Official)

◀54

▲55

55. US Navy cruisers and destroyers have the primary role of screening aircraft carriers from air and submarine attack; in wartime a small number would also be assigned to surface groups centred on *Iowa* Class battleships and a few to amphibious and underway replenishment groups. During 1983 there were nine nuclear-powered cruisers – including *California* (CGN-36), shown here in the Indian Ocean with the carrier *Nimitz* – and nineteen conventionally propelled cruisers in active service. (US Navy Official)

56. Now under construction are the *Ticonderoga* (CG-47) Class missile cruisers. These are the first warships with the advanced Aegis electronics/fire control system, and about 25 ships are expected to be completed, the first having joined the fleet in 1983. The Aegis cruisers have the same hull and propulsion plant as the *Spruance* (DD-963) Class anti-submarine destroyers. *Ticonderoga* displaces 9,200 tons full load and is 529ft long. (Ingalls Shipbuilding/Litton)

56 ▶

57 ▲

57. A technician inserts a block of radiating elements in a SPY-1A radar antenna. The 'building block' design permits different elements simultaneously to perform different functions, and to angle radar beams to provide wide coverage without the antenna itself having to rotate. The same radar will be used in the US Navy's new *Arleigh Burke* (DDG-51) Class missile destroyers. (RCA)

58. *Ticonderoga* reveals her similarity to her predecessors of the *Spruance* class in this overhead view as the ship steams at high speed. There are two fixed, six-sided antennae ('faces') for the SPY-1A multi-function radars on the forward and after superstructure. The SPY-1A provides simultaneous long-range search as well as precise target-tracking, and is highly resistant to electronic jamming. Note the Mk. 26 Standard missile launchers adjacent to the ship's 5in guns. (Ingalls Shipbuilding/Litton)

◄58

▲59

59. Cruisers and destroyers, as well as battleships and frigates, are now being provided with an 'offensive punch' in the form of Harpoon anti-ship cruise missiles, generally carried in four-canister sets; here a test craft fires a Harpoon from a set of canisters. Cruise missiles have 'low ship impact', that is they can be easily installed, unlike guns and missiles that require complex launchers and magazines. Later *Ticonderoga* Class cruisers and destroyers will have efficient vertical launchers for all types of missiles. (US Navy Official)

60. All but one of the US Navy's nine nuclear-propelled cruisers

completed between 1961 and 1980 are enlarged destroyer-type ships formerly designated DLGN. Here *Virginia* (CGN-38) shows off her large, uncluttered design. By Soviet and later US standards these 11,000-ton ships were under-armed, in part a result of the Navy's emphasis in nuclear ships being on their propulsion plant and not on their weapons or sensors. The new Soviet nuclear-propelled missile cruiser *Kirov* is more than twice as large as these vessels. (US Navy Official)

▼60

61▲

61. A stern view of *Texas* (GCN-39), one of the US Navy's nuclear cruisers. The smaller, conventionally propelled *Ticonderoga* Class ships have significantly more combat capability, owing to their Aegis/SPY-1A system and, in later ships, the vertical-launch systems for their missiles. (US Navy Official)
62. *Long Beach* (CGN-9), a 17,350-ton warship, is the US Navy's only true cruiser in active service. Completed in 1961, she was the sole ship of her design, being too expensive for series production. Proposals to provide an Aegis system were rejected by proponents of new nuclear cruisers who feared that modernizing her would lead to reduced cruiser construction. She has two surface-to-air missile launchers forward and eight Harpoon missiles aft as her main armament – little weaponry for a ship of her size. (Giorgio Arra)

62▼

▲63 ▼64

65▲

63. *Des Moines* (CA-134) is an 8in gun cruiser laid up 'in mothballs'. The Navy has a pair of these ships in reserve; along with the four *Iowa* Class dreadnoughts, they are the last big-gun warships afloat. There have been proposals to reactivate these cruisers, built just after the Second World War, but the battleships were judged to be more cost effective in terms of dollars and personnel. *Des Moines* and three sister-ships were, at 21,500 tons full load, the largest heavy (8in gun) cruisers ever built. (Giorgio Arra)

64. The Navy's eighteen older missile cruisers – *Jouett* (CG-29) is shown – have weapons and electronics similar to missile destroyers but are larger. The planned *Arleigh Burke* destroyers are intended to replace these ships as well as the existing missile destroyers, with some sixty vessels due to be retired during the 1990s. *Jouett* is 'single-end' missile ship, having a twin missile launcher forward and a helicopter hangar and deck and a 5in gun aft; 'double-enders' have missile launchers forward and aft. (US Navy Official)

65. An artist's concept of the *Arleigh Burke*. The first of these 8,500-ton ships is scheduled for completion in about 1990, and a further 60-plus are being planned. The final design will have only one 5in gun, plus Gatling-type guns, but ninety vertical launch tubes for anti-aircraft and anti-ship missiles, and the ships will operate with the *Ticonderoga* Class Aegis vessels in defence of carrier battle groups and battleship-centred surface action groups. (US Navy Official)

66. The modern Gatling gun is a 20mm cannon that has six barrels for firing bursts of bullets against attacking cruise missiles. The rate of fire is 3,000 rounds per minute, but the firing bursts last only a few seconds. The fire-control radar (white cylinder) automatically tracks targets and fires unless overriden by human command. These Gatling guns are being installed in all carriers, battleships and cruisers, and aboard most destroyers and amphibious ships. Electronic jamming and chaff rockets also protect ships against cruise missiles. (US Navy Official)

◀66

▲67 ▼68

67. The *Charles F. Adams* (DDG-2) Class missile destroyers, 23 vessels completed in the early 1960s, are regarded as excellent ships. They have two 5in guns plus a surface-to-air missile launcher (aft) and ASW rockets. However, they are 'tight' ships, limited in the amount of new electronic equipment they can accommodate, and lack helicopter facilities, now a vital component of anti-submarine operations. (US Navy Official)

68. Probably the most effective surface ASW ships in service today are the 31 *Spruance* Class destroyers. At 7,800 tons, these are large ships, and they served as the basis for four ships armed with surface-to-air missiles and the highly capable *Ticonderoga* Class cruisers. The ships' primary ASW 'weapons' – a large, bow-mounted SQS-53 sonar and the one or two ASW helicopters that can be carried aft – are not visible here. Note the large amount of electronics on the two lattice masts, necessary for a modern warship. (US Navy Official)

69. The stern aspect of a *Spruance* Class destroyer. Adjacent to the flight deck is a double hangar that can accommodate two ASW helicopters. The ship's bow-mounted sonar and a towed array can detect hostile submarines out to almost 100nm under certain conditions; close-in anti-submairne torpedoes can be launched over the side or fired by an ASROC missile out to a few miles, and at greater distances helicopters are guided to submarine contacts and attack with torpedoes. (US Navy Official)

70. Frigates are specialized ASW ships, the descendents of the Second World War frigates and destroyer escorts. They generally lack the more capable missiles, guns and electronic warfare equipment of cruisers and destroyers, but a shortfall in the number of those ships has led to frigates being employed to screen aircraft carriers. The Navy will soon have more frigates than any other type of warship – 115 will be in service by the late 1980s. (US Navy Official)

71. There are fifty *Oliver Hazard Perry* (FFG-7) Class frigates either in service or under construction for the US Navy, plus four ships for Australia. These are 3,710-ton ships of a not particularly attractive design. Forward there is a short-range surface-to-air missile launcher, amidships a 3in gun, and aft a Gatling gun and facilities for two ASW helicopters. While earlier frigates have a large, bow-mounted sonar, the *Perry* class have a small hull sonar plus a towed array sonar. (US Navy Official)

69▲

70▲   71▼

▲72   ▼73

72. An SH-60B Seahawk LAMPS III helicopter wearing the low-visibility markings now in vogue with US military forces. These ASW helicopters can also detect targets over the horizon (i.e. beyond radar range) for Harpoon anti-ship missiles, which can be fired from the ship's anti-aircraft missile launcher. The Navy's older frigates cannot handle the large Seahawk but normally carry one smaller SH-2F helicopter. (US Navy Official)

73. A *Knox* (FF-1052) Class ASW frigate moored alongside a destroyer tender and being painted by crew-men. The stern hatch, which can house a variable-depth or towed array sonar, is open. On the stern is a short-range Sea Sparrow defensive missile launcher, whilst forward of the Sea Sparrow is the helicopter deck and hangar. (Giorgio Arra)

74. An older ASW frigate, high and dry in a dock at a naval shipyard, displays the large SQS-26 series bow sonar dome (the SQS-53 in the *Ticonderoga* and *Spruance* Classes is similar). The 26/53 series can project an active acoustic signal to detect submarines out to almost 100nm with the proper water conditions; a passive towed sonar array can have even greater detection ranges, again under the right conditions. (US Navy Official)

74▶

▲75
75. An SH-2D ASW helicopter from a US warship overflies a Soviet task force off Gibraltar; a 'Foxtrot' class diesel submarine is below the helicopter. The US Navy has failed to develop a surface-ship 'stand-off' ASW weapon similar to the Anglo-Australian Ikara, French Malafon or Soviet SS-N-14; thus, since the early 1970s, when the available UH-2 Seasprite utility helicopters were converted to an ASW configuration, helicopters have provided the US Navy with its only stand-off anti-submarine capability. (US Navy Official)

▼76

76. A key component of the US Navy's anti-submarine forces is the maritime patrol/ASW P-3 Orion, a long-range, turboprop aircraft that can undertake missions of up to 17 hours duration. The plane is fitted with radar, sonobuoys, magnetic detection gear and optical sensors for locating submarines, and it can attack with torpedoes carried in an internal weapons bay or on wing stations. The P-3 can also deliver mines or nuclear depth bombs. (US Navy Official)

77. The US fleet is a combination of the old and new. This is due in part to the long period required to design and construct warships, and to their long services lives. Here the battleship *New Jersey* (BB-62), completed in 1943 and a veteran of three wars, fires a Tomahawk land-attack cruise missile following her return to the fleet forty years later. (US Navy Official)

78. A single 16in gun from *New Jersey*'s forward triple turret fires during the battleship's sea trials in 1982. While invaluable for supporting amphibious landings, *New Jersey* and her sister-ship *Iowa* will be more useful to the United States for political presence in forward areas. (US Navy Official)

79. (Next spread) The seven *Iwo Jima* (LPH-2) Class ships are 18,300-ton helicopter carriers that can accommodate 1,800 troops and twenty-odd helicopters, but these vessels do not have a landing craft or amphibious tractor capability. The ship's port deck-edge lift is shown in the lowered position. (US Navy Official)

▲ 80

80. A rare shot of *Blue Ridge* (left) and *Mount Whitney* underway. Shortly after this photograph was taken *Blue Ridge* was transferred to the Pacific, home-ported in Yokosuka, Japan, where she serves as the flagship of the US Seventh Fleet; *Mount Whitney*, based at Norfolk, Virginia, is the flagship of the US Second Fleet. (US Navy Official)

81. Conventional landing craft about to float out of the docking well of *Thomaston* (LSD-28); the ship is down by the stern and her docking well is flooded. (US Navy Official)

▼ 81

82. P-3 Orions are serviced in a former blimp hangar at Moffett Field Naval Air Station, near San Francisco, California; two Australian and two US Navy Orions are in the foreground. The P-3 is flown by several NATO air forces, plus Australia, Iran, Japan and New Zealand. The US Navy has 24 squadrons of nine aircraft each, while the Naval Reserve, which flies periodic patrols in company with the active units, has thirteen additional squadrons. (US Navy Official)

82 ▶

▲83　▼84

85▲

83. Mechanics servicing the Magnetic Anomaly Detector (MAD) equipment in the tail of a P-3. MAD detects the changes in the earth's magnetic field caused by the presence of a submerged submarine. The aircraft's tailfin markings consist of 'LU', indicating Patrol Squadron 64 (a reserve unit); the squadron's insignia, a buzzard emerging from 'VP-64'; and the aircraft's serial number. (US Navy Official)

84. An aircrewman prepares sonobuoys for ejection. The devices are parachuted to the water where an acoustic sensor is released; detection data is then radioed by the sonobuoy to the aircraft, where a computer plots the data and helps to determine the precise location of a submarine. (US Navy Official)

85. P-3 Orions are now being fitted with the Harpoon anti-ship missile; the weapons can be carried on wing stations so as not to interfere with the aircraft's ASW capability. During the Anglo-Argentine conflict in the Falklands in 1982 the British fitted their Nimrod maritime patrol aircraft to carry defensive Sidewinder air-to-air missiles. (McDonnell Douglas)

86. A P-3 Orion heads for home after a long patrol. A searchlight is fitted to one of the starboard wing stations. (US Navy Official)

86▼

▲87 ▼88

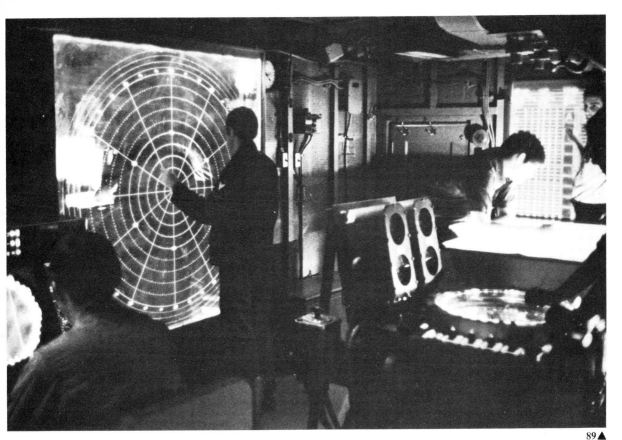

89▲

87. The command ships *Blue Ridge* (LCC-19) and *Mount Whitney* (LCC-20) are among the more unusual ships in the US Fleet. These vessels were designed to command amphibious operations, providing accommodation and command facilities for the amphibious force (Navy) and landing force (Marine) commanders and their staffs, but the shortage of large cruisers has led to their being assigned primarily as fleet flagships. Their predecessors were the US amphibious flagships and the British headquarters ships of the Second World War. (US Navy Official)

88. The command ship *Mount Whitney* seen off Norway during a NATO exercise. There is a US Marine UH-1 Huey helicopter on the stern landing deck, and a CH-46 Sea Knight hovers overhead. These ships' crews number about 500, with 'flag space' for more than 400, and, although well suited to command fleet as well as amphibious operations, they have a speed of only 20kts – suitable to keep up with amphibious task groups, but not for carrier operations – and have no hangar. (US Navy Official)

89. Sailors keep track of surface and sub-surface operations in one of the plots of the *Mount Whitney*. Most plotting is actually done in modern warships by computer, but the command ships have manual and computer plots to permit fleet and amphibious commanders to assess situations and make decisions. Satellites relay data on a 'real time' basis from shore command centres, from other ships, and from aircraft. (US Navy Official)

90. Most US surface-ship classes are shock-tested to determine their resistance to underwater blast. Here *Blue Ridge* is shown as an underwater blast begins to erupt during tests off the Pacific coast. (US Navy Official)

90▼

▲91

91. *La Salle* (AGF-3) is a former dock landing ship, extensively modified to serve as flagship of the Commander, US Middle East Force. She is the only white-painted ship in the US Navy and normally operates in the Persian Gulf and north-west Indian Ocean area. Since the occupation of the American embassy in Teheran in 1979 and the Soviet invasion of Afghanistan, the US Navy has kept at least one carrier battle group in the Indian Ocean. (US Navy Official)

92. The US Navy currently has 64 amphibious ships in service, three being assigned to the Naval Reserve Force with active-reserve crews. The largest of these ships are the *Tarawa* (LHA-1) Class helicopter carriers. *Saipan* (LHA-2) is one of five ships of this class, which displace 39,300 tons fully loaded and are 820ft long. They can embark some 2,000 Marines, landing them by the approximately thirty helicopters carried on board or by landing craft or amphibious tractors carried in a docking well. (US Navy Official)

93. This view of *Saipan* shows amphibious tractors 'swimming' out of the flooded docking well in the ship's stern. Note the helicopters parked on her flight deck, the large island superstructure laden with antennae and the opening for the stern lift (the dark rectangle between the flight deck and the docking well). The LHA and LPH ships have the flexibility of operating Harrier V/STOL attack aircraft, minesweeping helicopters and gunships, as well as troop-carrying helicopters. (US Navy Official)

▼92

93▶

▲94 ▼95

94. *Iwo Jima* (LPH-2) is the lead-ship of a class of seven smaller, 18,300-ton helicopter carriers than can embark about 1,800 troops and twenty-odd helicopters but not landing craft nor amphibious tractors. Like all other US amphibious ships, the helicopter carriers have a sustained speed of 20kts. (US Navy Official)

95. Marines scramble aboard CH-46 Sea Knight helicopters on the deck of a helicopter carrier. All US amphibious ships have helicopter decks, some having hangars for stowing a few machines. Airlifting is the most efficient way of landing troops and weapons, but the Marine Corps is developing a new series of amphibious tractors that will have a water speed of about 10kts and a limited ability to operate as personnel carriers on shore. (US Navy Official)

96. A Marine AV-8A Harrier V/STOL aircraft lands on the helicopter carrier *Tarawa* during operations off the Philippines; a CH-53 troop helicopter is aft. After several years of operating the AV-8A, the Marines are now buying 366 of the AV-8B Harrier II. British 'cousins' of these Harriers, Royal Navy Sea Harriers and Royal Air Force Harrier GR.3s, were very effective in the 1982 conflict over the Falklands. (US Navy Official)

96 ▼

97. A conventional landing craft comes into the docking well of *Fort Snelling* (LSD-30). The ship is down by the stern and her docking well is flooded. Several trucks and vans are parked on the ship's helicopter deck; some units are fitted with an expandable hangar. (US Navy Official)

98. Almost half of the Navy's amphibious ships are LPD and LSD 'wet well' ships, with docking wells that can accommodate landing craft and amphibious tractors. Here *Spiegel Grove* (LSD-32) takes aboard an air cushion landing vehicle, one of two prototypes of such craft. These craft, which are now in series production, can each carry an M60 tank on to a beach at a speed of 50kts. (US Navy Official)

99. The modern US Navy's tank landing ships, such as the *Tuscaloosa* (LST-1187), bear little resemblance to their Second World War predecessors. The unusual design permits 20kt speeds with shallow draught and a bow ramp for unloading tanks and other vehicles on to a beach or (more likely) pontoon causeways. Vehicles can be parked on a lower tank deck and driven up to the main deck by ramp or parked aft and driven through a tunnel in the superstructure, and there is also a stern ramp for unloading amphibious tractors into the water. (US Navy Official)

◄97

98▲   99▼

▲100　▼101

100. A Marine tank rolls through the surf towards a waiting LST, the latter's 112ft ramp extending through the open bow bulwarks, suspended by a derrick-like device. Although assault forces are landed by helicopter and amphibious tractor, the Navy still has twenty of these *Newport* (LST-1179) Class LSTs (US Navy Official)

101. LVTP-7 amphibious tractors waddle ashore from *Newport* Class LSTs during an amphibious exercise off the Californian coast. (US Navy Official)

102. Traditionally the US Navy has had little interest in small combatants. This is due, in part, to a desire to have ships that have trans-ocean operating ranges and multi-mission capabilities, two characteristics that lead to large ships. However, in the early 1970s the Chief of Naval Operations, Admiral E. R. Zumwalt, sought a programme of at least thirty hydrofoil patrol missile craft for operations in restricted areas such as the Mediterranean. In the event, only six were built, the lead-ship (shown) being *Pegasus* (PHM-1). (US Navy Official)

103. *Pegasus*, sitting high and dry, shows how her foils are raised when the ship is in a 'hull' or 'displacement' condition. The 231-ton, 147ft craft has diesels that can propel her at 12kts when hullborne and a gas turbine that can drive her at over 40kts when on foils. Armament consists of a 3in gun forward and eight Harpoon anti-ship missiles, in canisters, aft. (US Navy Official)

102 ▲   103 ▼

▲104   ▼105

106▲

104, 105. The hydrofoil missile craft *Taurus* (PHM-3) at high speed. An aircraft-type control system permits fast, smooth runs, so smooth in fact that a glass of water will not spill during a run at maximum speed. In this view only two single Harpoon canisters are fitted; an eight-missile armament gives these small craft considerable punch within their operating radius. (Boeing Marine Systems)

106. During the Vietnam War the US Navy built up a force of more than 700 coastal and riverine patrol craft, but most were turned over to South Vietnam and thus lost when the country fell. Today the US capability in this area consists of several reserve special boat units equipped with modern vessels such as these troop carriers and landing craft, shown during an exercise on the Chowan River in North Carolina. This force could be rapidly expanded should the United States again become involved in riverine/coastal combat operations. (US Navy Official)

107. The Navy's attitudes against small craft have carried over into mine warfare, and only now are the first minesweepers to be built since the Korean War under construction. Today the Navy has three active minesweepers plus eighteen ships manned by composite active-reserve crews, all built in the Korean War era. This is *Gallant* (MSO-489), which is assigned to the Naval Reserve force (NRF). (US Navy Official)

107▼

▲108

108. The Navy does have a significant airborne mine counter-measures capability, with RH-53D Sea Stallion helicopters that have been modified to sweep shallow-water mines. Here an RH-53D transfers minesweeping gear to *Illusive* (MSO-448). The Navy and Marine Corps are now acquiring the improved MH-53E, a three-engine heavy-lift version of the Sea Stallion that can be used for troop transport or minesweeping. The new helicopter can be refuelled in

flight, providing a trans-ocean ferry capability. (US Navy Official)
109. This close-up of *Fortify* (MSO-446), an NRF minesweeper, shows the traditional minesweeping gear on her fantail. These ships, built in the 1950s, have a very limited capability for countering modern naval mines, and with a top speed of 15kts they are too slow to respond rapidly to overseas mine threats. (US Navy Official)

▼109

110▲

110. This Vietnam-era photograph demonstrates the key to modern naval mobility – replenishment at sea. The fast combat support ship *Sacramento* (AOE-1, right) transfers fuel to an aircraft carrier off the coast of Vietnam while the AOE's UH-46 helicopters transfer aircraft fuel tanks to the carrier. (US Navy Official)

111. Day and night, in peace and in wartime, fleet oilers (AO) and combination oiler-replenishment ships (AOE and AOR) refuel warships at sea. Here the US Navy's civilian-manned fleet oiler *Taluga* (AO-62) refuels an aircraft carrier during heavy weather in the South China Sea. (US Navy Official)

111▼

112. Tenders provide a variety of services to other ships: destroyer tenders, for example, specialize in repairs and spare parts for surface ships and submarine tenders perform the same function for undersea craft. The largest ship shown here is the destroyer tender *Samuel Gompers* (AD-37), in Subic Bay, the Philippines, providing support to three nuclear cruisers – from the left, *Bainbridge* (CGN-25), *Truxtun* (CGN-35) and *Long Beach*. Note that CGN-25 and CGN-35, built as DLGNs, have destroyer hull lines, whilst the larger *Long Beach* has heavier, cruiser hull lines. (US Navy Official)

▲113

113. There are a number of different kinds of supply ship, generally categorized as Mobile Logistic Support Ships; in addition to fleet oilers and combination oiler-replenishment ships, there are refrigerated store ships (designated AF) and ammunition ships (AE). *Kilauea* (AE-26) shows the unusual lines of a modern supply ship, with refrigerated holds and transfer gear for ammunition and missiles forward and a helicopter facility aft to permit the resupply of distant warships. (US Navy Official)

114. Most of the US Navy's research and surveying ships are civilian-manned. Here *Chauvenet* (AGS-29), one of several British-built auxiliaries in the US fleet, is seen at Subic Bay in the Philippines. The ship carries a civilian crew numbering about seventy plus 12 civilian technicians and about 75 Navy personnel. The Navy men are survey specialists and maintain and fly the one or two helicopters assigned to the ship. (US Navy Official)

▼114

115. The US Navy maintains a small number of specialized cargo ships, such as the civilian-manned *Mercury* (AKR-11), a roll-on/roll-off vehicle cargo ship. During the past few years several of these ships, together with a number of chartered merchant ships, have been pre-positioned with military weapons and equipment at Diego Garcia in the Indian Ocean. During a crisis the vessels would move to a friendly port to be 'married up' with Marines flown there. Here *Mercury* loads Marine vehicles for the Rapid Deployment Force. (US Navy Official)

116. Among the Navy's miscellaneous auxiliaries is the gunnery-missile test ship *Norton Sound* (AVM-1), a converted seaplane tender. For more than 35 years she has been providing maritime tests of weapon and electronic systems, and currently she is conducting trials with the Aegis SPY-1 radar system and the vertical-launch missile system. (US Navy Official)

115▲ 116▼

▲117 ▼118

117. A number of ocean-going tugs and salvage ships are in service with the US Navy: here the fleet tugs *Takelma* (ATF-113, left) and *Moctobi* (ATF-105) manoeuvre *New Jersey* as the dreadnought is taken from reserve to a shipyard for reactivation in 1981. The salvage ships (ASR) and submarine rescue ships (ASR) are fitted to support deep-sea diving and salvage operations. (US Navy Official)

118. The Fleet has numerous bases along the US coasts as well as several major overseas facilities. Flotillas of small craft are used at these bases, most notably harbour tugs, a pair of which are shown at the huge Norfolk naval base struggling with the 'super carrier' *Nimitz*. The tugs' small masts are folded down to avoid being struck by the carrier's overhang, and note also the hemp fenders on *Wathena* (YTB-825) at left. A large number of the Navy's yard craft (hence 'Y'-series designations) have women sailors in their crews. (US Navy Official)

119, 120. Also found at most naval bases are floating dry docks; these are not self-propelled and are towed to forward areas. This photograph of *Oak Ridge* (ARDM-1) shows a strategic missile submarine being serviced. Note the two cranes that travel along tracks on top of the dock's 'sidewalls', structures which contain machine shops and equipment, including the dock's electric power generators. (US Navy Official)

121. (Overleaf) The US fleet is supported by a large complex of installations ashore – shipyards, naval bases, training centres, air stations, research laboratories, communication stations, supply facilities and, of course, various headquarters activities. There are eight naval shipyards, seven in the continental United States and one in Hawaii, at Pearl Harbor; these do not now construct ships but only overhaul and modernize them. The Long Beach yard is shown, refitting *New Jersey*. (US Navy Official)

119▲   120▼